CGP's non-fiction practice is the real deal!

This fantastic SAT Buster Book 2 from CGP is bursting with more essential
Non-Fiction Reading practice for the KS2 English SATs.

All the reading skills pupils need for the SATs are covered, with questions
based on a variety of non-fiction texts that'll really keep them engaged.

We've also included a helpful scoresheet at the back, so it's easy
to track progress and spot any areas they need to focus on.

What CGP is all about

Our sole aim here at CGP is to produce the highest quality books
— carefully written, immaculately presented and
dangerously close to being funny.

Then we work our socks off to get them out to you
— at the cheapest possible prices.

Contents

Section 1 –
The Angel of the North

Section 2 –
The Problem with Plastic

Section 3 –
From Sketches to Cinema

Section 4 –
Diving the Depths

Published by CGP

Editors: Tom Carney, Heather Cowley, Rachel Craig-McFeely, Sophie Herring and Gabrielle Richardson

ISBN: 978 1 78908 095 7

Printed by Elanders Ltd, Newcastle upon Tyne.
Clipart from Corel®

Based on the classic CGP style created by Richard Parsons.

The Angel of the North

This piece of non-fiction is about the Angel of the North, a large sculpture in the north-east of England. The text includes information about how the sculpture was built and why. Maybe you'll be inspired to visit it.

What to do

1) Open out the folding pages, and read the non-fiction text *The Angel of the North.*

2) Then read it again. It's the only way to be sure you've understood it all.

3) Spin around, touch your toes and do ten star jumps. You should now be ready to have a go at the questions.

Turn the page. ➡

Transporting the Angel

The sculpture was mostly built in Hartlepool, about 45 minutes' drive from Gateshead. This meant that the Angel had to be moved from one location to another when it was finished.

The Angel was so massive that the body and wings had to be driven on separate trailers and assembled at the end. The sculpture was still too large for some of the roads, so road signs and lampposts were temporarily removed to prevent a collision with the Angel as it passed. Even so, the journey took nearly five hours.

A North East icon?

The plans for the Angel initially divided opinion. The design caused controversy in the art world and some critics described it as hideous. Some local residents complained as well, arguing strongly that the Angel was a waste of money and an eyesore. People were also concerned about how safe it was. Some people claimed it might distract drivers and cause car accidents.

However, since it was built in 1998, the Angel's popularity has soared. Tourists visit the site to marvel at the remarkable sculpture up close, go for walks around it or picnic at its feet. Although there are still some who grumble at its unusual appearance, many locals love the huge sculpture and consider it an important landmark. In many ways, the Angel has become a symbol of the North East.

Love it or hate it, it's certainly a dramatic piece of visual art. Luckily, thanks to its location, millions of people every year can see the Angel and decide what they think about the sculpture for themselves.

Keep turning...

The Angel of the North

You might think that works of art belong in galleries or museums, so wouldn't expect to find one at the side of the road. Think again — that's exactly where you will find one of Britain's most iconic sculptures: the Angel of the North.

An Angel with a Difference

You can't miss the Angel if you're driving down the A1 motorway from Gateshead, a town in the north-east of England. For one thing, it is 20 metres high — that's taller than four double-decker buses. Its outstretched wings are even more impressive: they measure 54 metres, which is almost the same as the wings of a jumbo jet. The wings aren't white and feathery, and the sculpture doesn't wear a white robe or have a halo hovering above its head. Instead, it is a reddish-brown colour and made of steel, copper and concrete.

There is plenty of meaning behind this sculpture. Gateshead is known for its industrial heritage and many people from the area used to work in coal mining. The hill where the Angel stands is in an area where mining took place until the late 1960s. The local council chose this place as the Angel's location to honour the area's mining history.

Building the Angel

The Angel was designed by celebrated British artist Antony Gormley, who worked tirelessly with local engineers and companies to make his ambitious design a reality. He based the sculpture on a mould of his own body.

Due to the sheer size of the sculpture, the team had a challenge on their hands. If the Angel was constructed badly, it could have become unstable, particularly in strong winds. The team worked hard to find a solution and eventually came up with a plan. They placed hundreds of tonnes of concrete underneath the sculpture to support it. This means that the Angel is held firmly in place below the ground, so it won't topple over.

Fact Retrieval Questions

2b

FACT RETRIEVAL is all about getting down to the nitty-gritty of the text and pulling out key information. Have another look at the text, then have a go at the questions below.

1) The introduction tells us that the Angel of the North is located

| in a city | in a museum | by the side of a road | in Hartlepool |

Circle your answer.

_____
1 mark

2) Read the paragraph beginning **'You can't miss the Angel...'**
Give **one** mode of transport that the Angel is compared to.

....

_____
1 mark

3) Give **two** materials that the Angel is made from.

....

....

_____
2 marks

4) When did coal mining come to an end in the local area?

....

_____
1 mark

5) According to the text, who is Antony Gormley?

| an artist | an engineer | a local resident | a politician |

Circle your answer.

_____
1 mark

Here's what you have to do:

In Year 6 you have to take some tests called the SATs.
This book will help you do well in the reading bit of the tests.

The reading paper will test you on eight different reading elements:

2a Word Meanings   **2c** Summarising   **2e** Predictions   **2g** Language

2b Fact Retrieval   **2d** Inferences   **2f** Structure   **2h** Comparisons

These elements are used to see how well you can understand texts.

To help you improve your reading skills, this book has separate question pages for each of the reading elements — so you always know which one you are practising.

This is a Reading Raptor — it can read and understand even the trickiest non-fiction texts.

Your aim is to become a Reading Raptor.

Work through the questions in the book. When you finish a section, add up your marks and write them in the scoresheet at the end of the book.

Then, put a tick in the box at the end of the topic to show how you got on.

If you got a lot of questions wrong, put a tick in the circle on the left. Don't worry — every Reading Raptor has to start somewhere. Read the texts again carefully, then have another go.

If you're nearly there but you're still a bit wobbly on some questions, put a tick in the middle circle. Ask your teacher to help you work out the areas you need more practice on.

If you felt really confident and got nearly all the answers right, tick the circle on the right.

Congratulations — you're a Reading Raptor!

Fact Retrieval Questions

2b

6) According to the text, why is there concrete underneath the Angel?

| to make it taller | to stop it being blown over | to stop it sinking into the ground | to provide somewhere for picnics |

Circle your answer.

_____
1 mark

7) Why were lampposts and road signs temporarily removed from some roads?

....

_____
1 mark

8) Read the first paragraph of **'A North East icon?'**
Give **one** safety concern people had about the Angel.

....

_____
1 mark

9) Based on the text, give **two** things tourists do when they visit the Angel.

....

....

_____
2 marks

10) According to the final paragraph, why can **'millions of people'** see the Angel?
Tick **one** box.

It is very large.   ☐

It is near lots of houses.   ☐

It looks dramatic.   ☐

It is located near a motorway.   ☐

_____
1 mark

Reading Raptors can do fact retrieval questions with their eyes shut. How did you find them? Tick a box.

© CGP — not to be photocopied

Section 1 — The Angel of the North

2d

Inference Questions

INFERENCE questions are all about solving mysteries. You'll have to read the text closely and try to work out what is really being said. Try your hand at these questions.

1) Read the paragraph beginning **'You can't miss the Angel...'**
   Give **two** ways that the sculpture doesn't look like a traditional angel.

   ....

   ....

   2 marks

2) Why did the council want to **'honour the area's mining history'**? Tick **one** box.

   Many local people were miners. ☐

   Coal miners lived in Hartlepool. ☐

   The local council is based in an old mine. ☐

   Local miners built the statue. ☐

   1 mark

3) Read the paragraph beginning **'The Angel was designed...'**
   How can you tell that Antony Gormley was well-respected before he designed the Angel?

   Think about how Antony Gormley is described in the text.

   ....

   1 mark

4) Read the paragraph beginning **'Due to the sheer size of the sculpture...'**
   How can you tell that the building team was determined?

   ....

   ....

   1 mark

Inference Questions

2d

5) What evidence is there that the Angel was difficult to transport?

....

....

1 mark

6) Read the section called **'A North East icon?'**
How do you know that some local residents were angry about the plans to build the Angel?

....

1 mark

7) Put a tick in the correct box to show whether each statement is a fact or an opinion.

	Fact	Opinion
The Angel's wingspan is impressive.		
Tourists come to visit the sculpture.		
The Angel was a waste of money.		
Most of the sculpture was built in Hartlepool.		

1 mark

8) **'Love it or hate it, it's certainly a dramatic piece of visual art.'**
What does this suggest about people's attitudes to the Angel?

....

....

1 mark

Reading Raptors can do inference questions effortlessly, even really tricky ones. How did you get on?

© CGP — not to be photocopied

Section 1 — The Angel of the North

Word Meaning Questions

WORD MEANING questions put your vocabulary skills to the test. You'll need to think about what words really mean in the text. Have a go at the questions underneath.

1) **'...to make his ambitious design a reality.'**

   Circle the word that is closest in meaning to the word **'ambitious'**.

   | strange | difficult | expensive | frightening |

   1 mark

2) Look at the paragraph beginning **'The Angel was so massive...'**

   Find and copy **one** word which could be replaced with the word **'crash'**.

   ....

   1 mark

3) **'However, since it was built in 1998, the Angel's popularity has soared.'**

   What does the word **'soared'** mean in this sentence? Tick **one** box.

   increased slightly ☐

   stayed the same ☐

   risen by a lot ☐

   got worse ☐

   1 mark

4) **'Tourists visit the site to marvel at the remarkable sculpture up close...'**

   Which word in this sentence means 'admire'?

   ....

   1 mark

Reading Raptors eat word meaning questions for breakfast. How did you do with them?

Section 1 — The Angel of the North　　　　　　　*© CGP — not to be photocopied*

Summary Questions

SUMMARY QUESTIONS ask you about the general ideas in parts of the text. It's a good idea to reread 'The Angel of the North' before you start answering these questions.

1) Read the section called **'Building the Angel'**.

   Which sentence would you use to summarise this section?

The team overcame challenges.	The Angel was easy to build.	Antony Gormley is British.	Engineers are very clever.

   Circle your answer.

   _____
   1 mark

2) Read from **'The sculpture was mostly built...'** to **'...nearly five hours.'**

   This section is about

how to get to Hartlepool	where the Angel is located	moving the sculpture to Gateshead	the importance of art

   Circle your answer.

   _____
   1 mark

Prediction Question

You'll need your crystal ball for this one — PREDICTION questions ask you to look at the text and use it to make a sensible prediction about the future. Have a go at this one.

1) Based on the text, do you think the Angel will be around for a long time?

   Explain your answer as fully as you can.

   ....

   ....

   ....

   ....

   _____
   3 marks

Reading Raptors can see into the future. Can you?
How did you do with the questions on this page?

Section 1 — The Angel of the North

Fact Retrieval Questions

FACT RETRIEVAL questions ask you to get your magnifying glass out and search the text for information. Have another read through the text, then see if you can answer the questions.

1) Read the paragraph beginning **'Environmental campaigns occupy...'**
    Give **two** things that Nat Uremi didn't think about in the past when buying food.

    ....

    ....
    _____
    2 marks

2) Before her recent visit, when did Nat Uremi last go to her local beach?

    ....
    _____
    1 mark

3) Give **two** species of animal whose habitat has been ruined by litter on the beach.

    ....

    ....
    _____
    2 marks

4) Read the paragraph beginning **'I'm not alone, either...'**
    Give **two** things that British shoppers want, according to this paragraph.

    ....

    ....
    _____
    2 marks

5) Put a tick in the correct box to show whether each statement is true or false.

	True	False
Plastic food packaging helps to keep food fresh.		
We do not recycle any plastic.		
Plastic can take hundreds of years to break down.		
Animals can get trapped in litter.		

    _____
    1 mark

The Problem with Plastic

When it comes to the problem of plastic in our shops, reporter and proud environmentalist Nat Uremi is starting to see the issue in a new light.

Environmental campaigns occupy most of my free time now. I think you'd call me an 'eco-warrior'. However, I never used to give a second thought to how my behaviour could affect the world around me. I did my weekly food shop without ever considering what I was buying, where it was from or what packaging it came in.

That all changed, though, when I saw the impact of the amount of plastic we throw away. A few weeks ago, I visited my local beach for the first time in four years and saw the consequences for myself. What was once a thriving habitat for crabs, sea birds and a whole host of other seaside creatures had been transformed into a desert of litter. Plastic bags filled the rockpools where starfish used to live and discarded crisp packets covered the seaweed on the shore. It made me absolutely determined to do what I could to combat this critical issue.

I'm not alone, either — in recent years, British shoppers have woken up to the problem. There is a growing call to reduce plastic packaging and give shoppers more choice about how they buy their food and where it comes from.

The litter on Nat's local beach.

OUT WITH THE OLD, IN WITH THE RENEWABLE

When plastic food packaging was first introduced, it changed shoppers' habits. It meant that consumers could buy a huge range of food products and store them conveniently.

The text continues over the page.

Unfortunately, the plastic revolution has turned ugly. Although lots of plastic is recycled, the sheer scale of packaging produced means that a large proportion of plastic waste ends up in rubbish dumps. It can sit there for hundreds of years because it doesn't break down quickly like other materials. Animals can easily get trapped in larger items like carrier bags or mistake smaller items like bottle caps for food. It took us a long time to realise the extent of the damage, but now we know, we need to work together before it's too late.

One of the people leading the way is Claire Richards. She founded 'Hand-fill not Landfill' waste-free shops, and has just opened the doors of her second store. Unlike normal supermarkets, her shops stock individual, unpackaged items and food in large containers and jars, which customers can use to fill smaller containers to take home. Customers are encouraged to bring their own containers and bags with them, although these are available to buy in-store if anyone needs to stock up on them.

"Cotton bags and glass jars are the most popular choices," says Richards. "They're easy to clean and reuse, and most people already have some lying around their kitchens."

Claire Richards is passionate about reducing plastic packaging.

GIVING CHOICE A VOICE

As well as taking plastic waste out of the equation, Richards wants customers to be able to buy exactly what they need to avoid wasting food.

"At the end of the day, shopping should be about choice," Claire says. "There are so many products available to us — more than ever before — but supermarkets often sell products in bulk, meaning people buy far more than they need. My shops have scales down every aisle so that customers can weigh out precise

Many supermarkets still use a lot of plastic packaging.

amounts. It's a more cost-effective way of shopping and it helps to ensure that less food goes to waste."

SUPPORTING LOCAL

Claire has also made it her mission to encourage people to buy local produce. Her shops stock local products that can be easily traced back to individual farms.

"Buying local products reduces the environmental impact of transporting the food from the farm to the shop, as lorries have far shorter distances to travel. We are confident that all our products fit the bill, and we've done our research into where they come from," she tells me with a smile. "As well as becoming more aware of the plastic they may use, shoppers are also increasingly mindful of where their food comes from. By teaming up with local farmers, we can reassure our customers that they are making good choices."

There's still a long way to go, but initiatives like Claire's are a great place to start and I'll definitely be visiting her shops in the future. It might seem like one person's efforts are just a drop in the ocean, but when they're added together, we can create a tidal wave of change.

The Problem with Plastic

This text is a magazine article about the problem of plastic pollution and what could be done to fix the issue. It also talks about waste-free shops — shops where the products are not sold in any packaging.

What to do

1) Open out the folding pages, and read the non-fiction text *The Problem with Plastic.*

2) Now relax for a moment — imagine you're on holiday, you're lying on a beach and the sun is shining... Give the text another read as you're relaxing.

3) It's time to get back to reality and give the questions a try.

Turn the page.

Fact Retrieval Questions

2b

6) According to the text, what can animals mistake for food?

| carrier bags | crisp packets | pen lids | bottle caps |

Circle your answer.

———
1 mark

7) How many shops does Claire Richards own in total?

....

———
1 mark

8) Why are cotton bags and glass jars popular containers at Claire's shops? Give **two** reasons.

....

....

———
2 marks

9) How do Claire's shops help customers to buy the correct amount of food?

....

....

———
1 mark

10) Why does Claire choose to buy her produce locally?

....

....

———
1 mark

Reading Raptors have never got a fact retrieval question wrong. How did you do with them?

Section 2 — The Problem with Plastic

2d

Inference Questions

INFERENCE questions can be tricky — they're often less straightforward than other questions. Have a crack at these ones, bearing in mind that the answers might not be obvious.

1) How can you tell that Nat Uremi was shocked by her visit to the beach?

....

....

1 mark

2) Read the paragraph beginning **'I'm not alone, either...'**
   What evidence is there in this paragraph that people
   are concerned about plastic waste?

   Evidence is used to prove something. Look for a quote that proves people are worried.

....

....

1 mark

3) Read the paragraph beginning **'Unfortunately, the plastic revolution...'**
   This paragraph suggests that plastic waste is

   | safe | harmful | cheap | convenient |

   Circle your answer.

1 mark

4) Put a tick in the correct box to show whether each statement is
   a fact or an opinion.

	Fact	Opinion
Shopping should be about choice.		
Claire works with local farmers.		
Claire's shops have scales down every aisle.		
Claire's shops are better than other supermarkets.		

   1 mark

Inference Questions

2d

5) What does Claire Richards dislike about traditional supermarkets?

....

....

1 mark

6) Read the section called **'Supporting Local'**.
   Find and copy a phrase which suggests that buying local produce is important
   to Claire Richards.

....

1 mark

7) Read the paragraph beginning **'"Buying local products reduces...'**
   Tick the option that best matches your impression of Claire Richards
   at this point in the text.

   She doesn't care about what her customers think.   ☐

   She thinks lorries are eco-friendly.   ☐

   She doesn't know much about where food comes from.   ☐

   She is positive about the products she sells.   ☐

1 mark

8) How do you think Nat Uremi feels about Claire Richards's shops?
   Use evidence from the text to support your answer.

....

....

....

2 marks

*Reading Raptors can answer inference questions
quicker than the speed of light. What about you?*

2a

Word Meaning Questions

WORD MEANING questions do exactly what they say on the tin — they ask you what words
mean. Use the overall meaning of the sentences below to help you to answer the questions.

1) **'...do what I could to combat this critical issue.'**

What does the word **'critical'** mean in this sentence? Circle your answer.

important	boring	expensive	rare

1 mark

2) **'...consumers could buy a huge range of food products and store them**
conveniently.'

Circle the word that means the same as **'conveniently'** in this sentence.

slowly	carefully	easily	regularly

1 mark

3) **'My shops have scales down every aisle so that customers can weigh out**
precise amounts.'

Which word in this sentence could be replaced with the word 'exact'?

....

1 mark

4) **'"Buying local products reduces the environmental impact of transporting**
the food from the farm to the shop..."'

What does the word **'transporting'** mean in this sentence?

....

1 mark

Reading Raptors know what every word means.
How did you find these questions?

The last few questions on __The Problem with Plastic__ are under here. ➤

Section 2 — The Problem with Plastic   *© CGP — not to be photocopied*

It's FACT RETRIEVAL time! Get your fact detector out, search the text and see what you can dig out. Keep your facts safe and then answer the questions.

1) Who are animated films aimed at nowadays?

....

_____
1 mark

2) Read the first paragraph.

Give **two** things that animated films can be about.

....

....

_____
2 marks

3) Which of the following is **not** part of a storyboard?

| written notes | some drawings | music and sound effects | dialogue ideas |

Circle your answer.

_____
1 mark

4) Why are storyboards used? Tick **one** box.

To show who has made the animation ☐

To make sure everyone making the film knows the plot ☐

To make money early on in the production process ☐

To tell parents if the film is suitable for children ☐

_____
1 mark

5) How many facial expressions are shown on each model sheet?

....

_____
1 mark

Summary Questions

2c

SUMMARY questions ask you to work out what the main points of a text are.
Read 'The Problem with Plastic' one more time, then have a go at these questions.

1) Which of these sentences is the main idea of **'Giving Choice a Voice'**?
Tick **one** box.

There are lots of supermarkets in Britain. ☐

You should no longer shop at supermarkets. ☐

Claire thinks people should choose how much they want to buy. ☐

Supermarkets sell lots of products. ☐

1 mark

2) The section called **'Supporting Local'** is about

| going to local shops | cleaning your local area | recycling | buying local products |

Circle your answer.

1 mark

Language Question

2g

For LANGUAGE questions, you need to get into the author's mind and think about why they've chosen the words they've used. See how you get on with the question below.

1) **'...Nat Uremi is starting to see the issue in a new light.'**
Why do you think the writer chose the phrase **'see the issue in a new light'**?

> Make sure you suggest why the phrase was used — don't just write out what it means.

....

....

1 mark

Language and summary questions are all in a day's work for Reading Raptors. How did you get on?

© CGP — not to be photocopied

Section 2 — The Problem with Plastic

Behind the doors of the Production Department

We asked Ashley Hale, a Concept Artist who works in the Production Department, to tell us more about how her department works. Read on as she shines a spotlight on her job...

Hi, Ashley.
Can you start by explaining what your job involves?
Of course. I work as part of the team that produces the model sheets for the film, so I spend lots of time sketching faces. The human face is capable of a whole host of expressions, and an animated one is no different. We work hard on every small detail and we can't cut corners. I regularly attend meetings with my colleagues where we review each other's work to make sure we keep standards high.

What happens if a drawing is proving problematic?
That's absolutely fine and practically inevitable! If I'm struggling with an aspect of a character, I have a talented team of people around me to call upon for advice. It's definitely a team effort.

Have you always been a Concept Artist?
Not at all. After university, I got a job as a Runner. Basically, I took messages from department to department, changed light bulbs and made the Director lots of cups of tea! It sounds exhausting, but I made friends with the Animators and showed them some of my drawings. I'm really glad I did because when they needed a new Concept Artist, they asked me to step up to the mark. I take a lot of pride in my work and love to see the finished film on screen.

Clay models take shape

Once the Production Department has produced the model sheets, they create clay models from the 2D drawings. This helps everyone on the team to picture what the characters look like in 3D. The team also creates vehicles, props and whole buildings out of clay to see how they will look from every angle. Piece by piece, the film's world starts to come to life.

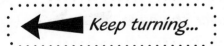

Keep turning...

From Sketches to Cinema

Thanks to new technology, animation is one of the fastest-growing industries in the world. No longer aimed solely at children, animated films are now designed with the whole family in mind. Whether they're about secret superheroes, friendly fish or talking toys, these films dazzle us with their special effects and imaginative characters. But how are these animated films created, and who dreams up these fascinating stories? Read on for a rare glimpse inside the world of the animation studio!

From plan to paper

The first step in any animated film is the storyboard. This is similar to a comic strip: it's a series of sketches that show the story unfolding, step by step. Written notes and dialogue ideas are added too. Since most animated films are produced by large teams of people, storyboards ensure that everyone knows the plot of the film.

The storyboard is the first step of an animated film.

Detailed designs

Once a storyboard is agreed, it's time to start work on the detail. The Layout Department cooperates with the Director to decide how every setting will look. This team is responsible for designing all of the locations in the film, from bustling city streets to colourful coral reefs. A film will have many different locations, so it's important to pin these down early on.

Model sheets show a wide range of expressions.

At the same time, the Production Department gets to work on the model sheets. These are very detailed drawings showing the full range of a character's possible facial expressions: from upset to overjoyed, and from furious to relaxed. There are usually between 10 and 15 expressions per character. It's essential that characters look consistent across the whole film, so these drawings become the template for their face.

The text continues over the page.

From Sketches to Cinema

This text is about animation. It contains information about the process of creating an animated film. It also includes an interview with a Concept Artist who works in the animation industry.

What to do

1) Read the non-fiction text *From Sketches to Cinema* — you'll need to turn over for some of it.

2) Then have another read over it — make sure you take everything in.

3) Think about your favourite animated film — maybe it's about a superhero or a unicorn. Then answer the questions.

The computers come in

Believe it or not, all animations are actually a clever trick. They are a series of pictures, viewed so rapidly that they appear to be moving. These pictures are called frames, and there are 24 of them every single second. It's easy to forget this when you're watching an animation because the frames fit together so smoothly.

However, making these frames used to be very time-consuming. When the first animated films were made in the late 1800s, every frame was drawn by hand. They were photographed individually and combined to give the illusion of a moving picture.

Nowadays, frames can be created efficiently on a computer using specialist software. The Editorial Team uses the storyboard to add music, sound effects and voice recordings. This has to be impeccably timed to make sure that all of the elements will fit together, otherwise the animation won't seem very realistic. It's no good if a character's voice doesn't match the way their mouth moves.

At the same time, the Animators create the digital characters. Using the model sheets and clay mock-ups for guidance, they bring the characters to life, frame by frame. Other Animators produce digital versions of the buildings, vehicles and props created by the Production Department, before adding textures, reflections and shadows so that everything looks true to life.

What's next?

Before the animation is done and dusted, all the elements need to be combined and checked. Editors make sure that the film flows properly and that all of the sound and action combines to create a believable world — the audience should be able to lose themselves in the story. Editors also remove any unwanted scenes: there are thousands of frames that don't make the final cut, otherwise the film would be much too long. Finally, the credits are added and the animation is then ready for an audience. Roll out the red carpet!

Animations should capture the audience's attention.

← Open the flap for the start of the text.

Fact Retrieval Questions

2b

6) Put a tick in the correct box to show whether each statement is true or false.

	True	False
Model sheets are made before clay models.		
Characters' faces don't have to look consistent.		
Animated films only have one location.		
The Production Department creates clay models.		

1 mark

7) Read the interview with Ashley Hale.

What does Ashley do if she's having trouble with a drawing?

....

....

1 mark

8) What was Ashley Hale's job after she left university?

....

1 mark

9) Read the section called **'The computers come in'**.

In modern animations, how many frames are shown in each second?

....

1 mark

10) According to the text, what is the last thing that happens before a film is ready?

....

1 mark

Reading Raptors can find a fact in a haystack.
How are your fact-finding skills coming along?

Section 3 — From Sketches to Cinema

2d Inference Questions

INFERENCE questions are about things that aren't immediately obvious when you first read the text. They will make you think carefully about what's being said — have a go at these.

1) Read the first paragraph.

What evidence is there that animated films are very popular nowadays?

....
_____
1 mark

2) The first paragraph suggests that finding out about what happens in an animation studio is

| boring | easy | tiring | exciting |

Circle your answer.
_____
1 mark

3) When the writer says '**The first step in any animated film is the storyboard**', are they stating a fact or giving an opinion?

....
_____
1 mark

4) Why do you think Ashley Hale says '**we can't cut corners**'?

| **Animations are easy to make.** | **They can't cut their clay models.** | **Their work needs to be high quality.** | **She wants to be an Animator.** |

Circle your answer.
_____
1 mark

5) Read the interview with Ashley Hale.

How can you tell that Ashley cares about producing good animations?

Support your answer with evidence from the text.

....

....

....
_____
3 marks

Inference Questions

6) Read the paragraph beginning **'Once the Production Department has...'**
   Find and copy a phrase from the text which shows that the film comes
   together slowly.

   ....
   ....
   1 mark

7) Read the section called **'The computers come in'**.
   Why do you think the author calls animations **'a clever trick'**?

   Think about how
   animations are made.

   ....

   ....
   ....
   1 mark

8) Read the paragraph beginning **'However, making these frames...'**
   What evidence is there that making animated films was difficult in the past?

   ....

   ....

   ....
   ....
   2 marks

9) **'It's no good if a character's voice doesn't match**
   the way their mouth moves.' Why do you think this is?

   ....
   ....
   1 mark

Inference questions are second nature to
Reading Raptors. How were they for you?

© *CGP — not to be photocopied*   *Section 3 — From Sketches to Cinema*

Word Meaning Questions

I hope you've been reading your dictionary, because if you want to get these WORD MEANING questions right, you'll need to know what words mean. See how you get on with them.

1) **'...these films dazzle us with their special effects...'**

   Circle the word that is closest in meaning to the word **'dazzle'**.

calm	scare	amaze	teach

   _____
   1 mark

2) Look at the section called **'Detailed designs'**.

   Find and copy **one** word from this section which could be replaced with

   the phrase 'works together'.

   ....

   _____
   1 mark

3) **'I have a talented team of people around me...'**

   What does the word **'talented'** mean in this sentence?

   ....

   _____
   1 mark

4) **'They were photographed individually and combined to give the illusion of a moving picture.'**

   What does the word **'illusion'** mean in this sentence? Tick **one** box.

   audience ☐

   order ☐

   variety ☐

   appearance ☐

   _____
   1 mark

---

*Word meaning questions are a doddle for
Reading Raptors. How many words did you know?*

....
The last few questions on From Sketches to Cinema are under here. ➡
....

Although scuba equipment has come on in leaps and bounds, freediving continues to appeal today: it requires no complicated equipment and connects the diver more closely to their surroundings. Freediving also poses more of a physical test to divers, and modern freedivers have challenged themselves to reach seemingly impossible depths. Athletes like the Austrian Herbert Nitsch and Natalia Molchanova, a Russian world champion known as 'The Queen', have pushed the human body to its limits by achieving incredible feats such as diving to over 100 metres below the surface without an air tank. Their staggering achievements would have seemed unthinkable to divers of the past. Because of its challenges, freediving is also very dangerous, even for professional divers.

Spending long periods of time underwater, with or without oxygen, takes its toll on a diver's body. Decompression sickness, or 'the bends', can occur if a diver swims to the surface too quickly. This can result in headaches, joint pains and dizziness. Fortunately, divers have come up with clever ways to lower the risk — they make sure they are well-hydrated and rise slowly to the surface, taking frequent breaks so their bodies have time to adjust.

The stress diving puts on the body makes safety a priority. It is all too easy to become disorientated underwater, with no obvious points of reference, so divers always swim with a buddy. Hand signals and underwater writing slates are used to constantly communicate and monitor one another's safety. Even in warm water, a diver's body temperature can drop dangerously low, so divers wear wetsuits to avoid getting too cold.

Even with its risks, there is no doubt that diving offers human beings a unique perspective on our planet. Whether in the name of science or recreation, the underwater world has an irresistible charm that has divers of all kinds returning to the oceans again and again. And we've barely got started: it is estimated that we have only explored 5-10% of the Earth's oceans, and that thousands of underwater species are still entirely unknown to us. Who can say what mysterious secrets the deepest seas may hold?

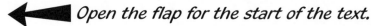

← *Open the flap for the start of the text.*

Diving the Depths

This text is about underwater diving. It describes the history of diving, as well as the difference between scuba diving and freediving. It also contains information about why people choose to go diving and what precautions they need to take to stay safe underwater.

What to do

1) Read the non-fiction text *Diving the Depths* — you'll need to turn over for some of it.

2) Pretend to make yourself an ice-cold drink, and gulp it down as quickly as you can.

3) Once you're feeling refreshed, read the text again, then turn over and have a go at the questions.

Diving the Depths

With almost three-quarters of the world's surface covered in water, it's no surprise that humans have been endlessly fascinated by the Earth's oceans. For thousands of years, we have explored our underwater environments, from the warm tropical shallows of the Caribbean Sea to the icy depths of the Arctic Ocean. One of the most exciting ways to explore the oceans is through diving. Free from the cramped cabin of a submarine, divers can experience the sights and sensations of an enchanting underwater world — luminous fish and plants, shimmering glimpses of sunlight and a tranquil feeling of weightlessness.

Diving the oceans has improved our knowledge of them immensely and now plays a vital role in their conservation. It allows scientists to get close to rare or endangered ocean species, such as coral, in order to study them. This provides the first-hand information scientists need to track the health of different ocean dwellers. When footage of these dives is televised, it often captures the public's imagination and educates us all about the importance of protecting our seas and their inhabitants.

The text continues over the page.

Conservation isn't the only reason that people choose to enter the oceans: for many people, diving is their livelihood. Diving tourism is now a thriving industry, with professional instructors across the world teaching people how to dive safely. Towns such as Hurghada, an Egyptian resort on the Red Sea, have had their fortunes turned around by diving tourism. Originally a small fishing village, tourists have transformed the town into a busy economic centre and the number of hotels and diving businesses has skyrocketed since the 1980s.

Diving tourism is a fairly recent phenomenon. Before the tourism boom, merchants employed divers for more practical reasons: to search the seabed for valuable goods that they could sell. In years gone by, divers would regularly take their life in their hands to harvest oysters and pearls from the seabed by hand. There are also stories of Ancient Greek divers being sent deep underwater to retrieve expensive possessions from sunken ships to be sold on.

Of course, the divers of Ancient Greece were equipped very differently to those of today. Firstly, they would have been freedivers. Put simply, freediving is breath-hold diving: the diver takes a breath before they descend, which they hold until they surface again. By contrast, modern scuba divers use specialist equipment, such as oxygen tanks and face masks, to allow them to breathe underwater.

Scuba diving equipment has evolved considerably since the earliest designs were drawn up. Leonardo da Vinci designed a leather diving suit in around 1500, though it was probably never made. It wasn't until 1865 that engineers began experimenting with air tanks that could be sent underwater with the diver. Many tried, and in 1943, two French engineers, Jacques-Yves Cousteau and Émile Gagnan, were successful. The 'Aqua-lung' was the first modern scuba design to become popular across the world, and a similar component is still part of almost every set of scuba gear today.

Keep turning...

Summary Question

SUMMARY questions make you think about sections of a text and the text as a whole. It's a good idea to reread the whole text before you start answering this question.

1) Read from **'However, making these frames...'** to **'...match the way their mouth moves.'**

   How can these paragraphs be summarised?

Animation is a new process.	**Sound effects need to be added.**	**Animation must be realistic.**	**Technology has changed animation.**

   Circle your answer.

   1 mark

Structure Questions

STRUCTURE questions are all about the way information is organised in the text. Think about why the writer has organised it that way. Take a look at these questions and have a go.

1) Write the numbers 1 to 4 in the boxes to put these parts of the text in the right order. The first one has been done for you.

   Creating model sheets [ ]

   Adding sound [ ]

   Creating frames [ ]

   Designing a storyboard [1]

   Read over the text again and make a note of when each process happens.

   1 mark

2) Why is the text structured in this order?

   ....

   ....

   1 mark

Reading Raptors are tip-top when it comes to summary and structure questions. How did you do?

Section 3 — From Sketches to Cinema

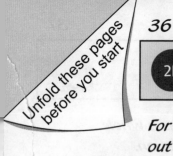

2b **Fact Retrieval Questions**

For FACT RETRIEVAL questions, go over the text with a fine-tooth comb to pick out any relevant information. Read the text closely and answer the questions.

1) How much of the world's surface is covered in water?

....

1 mark

2) Read the first paragraph.
Give **two** examples of things divers can see underwater.

....

....

2 marks

3) According to the text, what happens when diving footage is shown on TV?

....

....

1 mark

4) Read the paragraph beginning **'Diving tourism is a fairly recent phenomenon...'**
What did Ancient Greek divers collect from the sea?

| fish | valuable objects | boats | pearls |

Circle your answer.

1 mark

5) What is 'freediving'?

| scuba diving | deep-sea diving | diving without air tanks | diving with a buddy |

Circle your answer.

1 mark

Fact Retrieval Questions

6) a) Name **one** of the inventors of the 'Aqua-lung'.

....

1 mark

b) When was it invented?

....

1 mark

7) Which of the following facts can be found in this text? Tick **two** boxes.

Freediving requires no heavy equipment. ☐

You cannot wear flippers while freediving. ☐

Herbert Nitsch is a Russian diver. ☐

Natalia Molchanova was a world champion. ☐

People have dived up to 200 metres below the surface. ☐

1 mark

8) How do divers avoid decompression sickness? Give **two** ways.

....

....

2 marks

9) Read the paragraph beginning **'The stress diving puts on the body...'**
What do divers do to make sure they stay safe underwater? Give **three** things.

....

....

....

3 marks

Reading Raptors retrieve any fact that needs retrieving. How many facts did you find?

Inference Questions

For INFERENCE questions, you'll need to dig deep to uncover hidden information. So dust off your bucket and spade, and start digging. The questions below should be good practice.

1) Read the first paragraph.

   How can you tell that the writer doesn't like submarines?

   > *Think about how the writer describes submarines.*

   ....

   1 mark

2) Read the paragraph beginning **'Diving the oceans...'**

   Find and copy a phrase which suggests that diving is helpful for ocean conservation.

   ....

   1 mark

3) Put a tick in the correct box to show whether each statement is a fact or opinion.

	Fact	Opinion
Diving is the best way to explore the oceans.		
Diving has improved our knowledge of the oceans.		
Some scientists study coral.		
Rare species are the most interesting to see.		

   1 mark

4) What evidence is there that Hurghada is a popular place to go on holiday?

   ....

   ....

   1 mark

5) Read the paragraph beginning **'Diving tourism...'**

   How do you know that diving for pearls is dangerous?

   ....

   ....

   1 mark

Inference Questions

2d

6) Read the paragraph that begins **'Scuba diving equipment...'**
   How do you know that designing scuba diving equipment was difficult?

   ....

   ....

   1 mark

7) Read the paragraph beginning **'Although scuba equipment...'**
   Why do some people choose freediving over scuba diving? Circle your answer.

   | It is more modern. | It is more challenging. | You can dive deeper. | You can do it anywhere. |

   1 mark

8) How do you think the writer feels about Herbert Nitsch and Natalia Molchanova?
   Support your answer with evidence from the text.

   ....

   ....

   1 mark

9) Read the paragraph beginning **'Spending long periods of time underwater...'**
   Find and copy a phrase which suggests that diving is physically demanding.

   ....

   1 mark

10) How do you think the writer feels about the risks of scuba diving?
    Explain your answer with reference to the text.

   ....

   ....

   ....

   3 marks

*Reading Raptors can do inference questions
standing on their head. How did you do?*

Section 4 — Diving the Depths

Word Meaning Questions

In WORD MEANING questions, you have to get to the bottom of what words mean in context. Read the sentence each word belongs to before you answer the questions below.

1) **'...humans have been endlessly fascinated by the Earth's oceans.'**
   What does the word **'fascinated'** mean in this sentence?

shocked	interested	scared	amused

   Circle your answer.

   _____
   1 mark

2) Read the paragraph beginning **'Diving the oceans...'**
   Find and copy a word from this paragraph that means 'hugely'.

   ....
   _____
   1 mark

3) **'Diving tourism is now a thriving industry...'**
   What does the word **'thriving'** mean in this sentence? Tick **one** box.

   new ☐

   successful ☐

   limited ☐

   smaller ☐

   You need to choose the word that is a synonym of thriving

   _____
   1 mark

4) **'...taking frequent breaks so their bodies have time to adjust.'**
   What does **'frequent'** mean in this sentence?

   ....
   _____
   1 mark

Reading Raptors know what every word means.
How do you compare to a Reading Raptor?

Summary Questions

2c

SUMMARY questions aren't just about individual words and phrases — they're about big chunks of the text. Bear that in mind when you reread the text and tackle the questions.

1) Read from **'Conservation isn't the only reason...'** to **'...sunken ships to be sold on.'**

Circle the statement which best summarises this part of the text.

Diving started in the 1980s.	Diving is suitable for all ages.	Diving is expensive for tourists.	People dive for different reasons.

1 mark

2) Read from **'Spending long periods of time...'** to **'...avoid getting too cold.'**

Which of these sentences is the main idea of this part of text? Tick **one** box.

Freediving is too dangerous. ☐

Divers usually run out of oxygen. ☐

Diving can be dangerous unless precautions are taken. ☐

Freedivers can dive deeper than scuba divers. ☐

1 mark

Comparison Question

2h

COMPARISON questions ask you to write about things that are similar or different in the text. You need to take a close look at the text before answering them. Have a go at this question.

1) How has diving changed over time? Use evidence from the text in your answer.

....

....

....

2 marks

Reading Raptors click their fingers and the summary and comparison questions are done. What about you?

Scoresheet

Great work, you're all finished with this book. Use the answer book to find out how well you did and write your marks in the table below.

	Section 1 – The Angel of the North	Section 2 – The Problem with Plastic	Section 3 – From Sketches to Cinema	Section 4 – Diving the Depths	Total
2a Word Meanings	/ 4	/ 4	/ 4	/ 4	/ 16
2b Fact Retrieval	/ 12	/ 14	/ 11	/ 14	/ 51
2c Summarising	/ 2	/ 2	/ 1	/ 2	/ 7
2d Inferences	/ 9	/ 9	/ 12	/ 12	/ 42
2e Predictions	/ 3				/ 3
2f Structure			/ 2		/ 2
2g Language		/ 1			/ 1
2h Comparisons				/ 2	/ 2
Total	/ 30	/ 30	/ 30	/ 34	/ 124

Look at your total score to see how you're doing and where you need more practice:

0 – 55 — Don't worry if you got lots wrong. Revise the reading skills you're struggling with and then have another go at the questions.

56 – 100 — You're doing well. Look back at any reading elements you're struggling with and try the questions again to make sure you're happy with them.

101 – 124 — Good work, you're doing great. Give yourself a pat on the back.